The Wolf

by Megan Howard
illustrated by John Nez

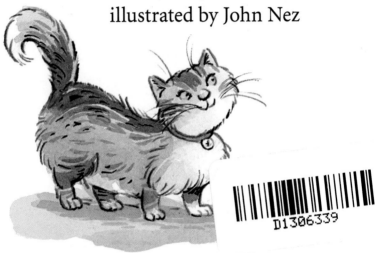

Table of Contents

CHAPTER 1
Dinner

"Katie, you haven't eaten any dinner," my grandmother said. She was right. All the potatoes were still on my plate. The broccoli still looked like little trees. And I had eaten very little of my chili.

Granny was traveling to Europe the next day. She was going to stay on a sheep farm in Ireland for a month. Granny had a passion for traveling. But I was worried about this trip.

"There might be wolves near the sheep," I told her. "It could be dangerous."

"You've read too many fairy tales about wolves," Granny said.

I had read lots of fairy tales. But I had also read many nonfiction books. And I had learned about sheep. "Wolves eat sheep," I said.

"That sounds awful," Granny joked. My grandmother did not eat meat. "I promise to watch out for wolves," Granny said.

I felt better. I wanted Granny to be careful.

After dinner, we washed the dishes.

"I'll send you pictures from Ireland," Granny told me.

"Will you e-mail me every night?" I asked.

"Yes," she said. Granny always sent me an e-mail to say good night.

"I admire you because you explore the world," I told her.

Suddenly, I felt soft fur rubbing against my ankles. It was Granny's cat, Ribbon. "I'll take good care of Ribbon while you're away," I said.

"I know you will," Granny said. "Now go home and do your homework. I have to get ready for my trip tomorrow. Bundle up. It's raining hard outside."

I put on my red raincoat and boots. Then I rushed home through the rain.

CHAPTER 2
A Strange Message

The next afternoon, I ran all the way home from school. When I got home, my legs ached. I rushed to the computer. My father was already using it.

"Can I check if Granny sent me an e-mail?" I asked without bothering to take off my backpack.

"I have to work, Katie," Dad said.

"What if something funny happened to Granny on the airplane? She'll want to tell me," I said.

"Okay, you can use the computer,"
my father said. "Let's check your e-mail."

I dropped my backpack on the floor.
I sat down next to Dad at the computer.
There were no new e-mails from Granny.

Clue: I is the subject in this sentence. What
is the sentence's predicate?

Suddenly, I got an e-mail. It came from someone named Ima Wolf. "Hi!" the e-mail said.

"I'm a wolf?" I laughed. "It is Granny joking about wolves."

I typed a response. "Are you Granny?"

"Yes," Ima Wolf answered.

"How are you?" I asked.

The reply came back quickly. It said, "Hungry."

"How is your vacation?" I typed.

Her answer surprised me. "I'm not on vacation. I'm home," it said.

What happened? "Why are you still home?" I asked.

"Because I'm sick," Ima Wolf replied.

Poor Granny was sick! "You should have called Dad," I wrote.

"I'm also hungry," Ima Wolf wrote.

"I'll bring you something to eat," I wrote back. "What do you want?"

"Lamb stew," Ima Wolf answered.

Granny never ate meat! Was Ima Wolf someone pretending to be Granny?

Dad and I decided to find out if Ima Wolf was really Granny.

CHAPTER 3
Katie and the Wolf

If Ima Wolf was Granny, she would be able to e-mail me a picture of something in her house.

"Granny, please e-mail me a picture of Ribbon," I typed.

"I don't have any ribbon," Ima Wolf answered.

I had tricked Ima Wolf! Granny would have known what Ribbon was.

"Ribbon is your cat," I wrote.

"Oh, yes. I forgot because I'm sick," she answered.

"A really sick person could have gotten confused," I said to Dad.

Then a photo of Ribbon appeared on my computer.

"Maybe it really is Granny," I said. How could we know for sure?

Then I had a splendid idea! I asked Granny to send me a photograph of herself. A picture appeared on the screen. It was blurry. I could not see the face clearly.

Clue: Screen is a multiple-meaning word. What are two meanings of *screen*?

Folder

"Granny, your eyes are so big," I typed.

"That's because I am sick," she wrote.

"And your nose is so long," I typed.

"Don't be mean," Ima Wolf responded.

"And your teeth are so pointy," I wrote.

"I have new false teeth," she explained.

"Why do you have fur all over your face?"

Ima Wolf did not answer. There was someone in Granny's house, but it wasn't Granny!

Who was in Granny's house? I tried to concentrate on the photograph. Then I realized that it was a wolf!

Dad called the police. Then we went over to Granny's house.

I was right! We saw two police officers leaving Granny's house with a wolf.

When I got home, I saw an e-mail from Granny. It said, "Katie, I miss you so much. I have seen a lot of sheep. Luckily, I have not seen any wolves."

Comprehension Check

Summarize the Story

Complete the Compare and Contrast Chart with the class. Then summarize the story. Use the chart to help you organize your ideas.

Alike	Different

Think and Compare

1. Review the story. Which parts of the story could be real? Which parts could not be real? *(Compare and Contrast)*

2. What do you admire about your grandparents or other older relatives? Explain why. *(Evaluate)*

3. Why is it important to know who you are talking to on the Internet? *(Apply)*